Aromatic Aphrodisiac: the pure fragrance of essential oils distilled from the petals of a flower, the surface of a leaf, the rind of a fruit, the roots, resin or heartwood of a tree and used since antiquity to enhance the sensuous pleasures of romantic and erotic love.

Publisher: Capricorn Press Ltd.
6 Adelaide Crescent, Hove, East Sussex BN3 2JE, UK
Book Design: Gary Thompson, Brighton, UK
Printing: Colourspeed, Segensworth East, UK

ISBN 0954-7080-1-6

Disclaimer: Neither the author nor the publisher are responsible for any side effects that may occur through information presented in this book. Essential oils are not for internal use.

Printed in the UK

Releasing Aphrodite

Aromatic Aphrodisiacs for Love and Romance

ELISABETH MILLAR

Capricorn Press Ltd.
Hove, UK

To the men I love

Very special thanks to Ann Woodhead and Barbara Grehs for their invaluable help in the creation of *Releasing Aphrodite*, and especially to Ann for providing the exquisite essential oil recipes it contains.

Dear Reader,

I often wonder why so many of us – independent, intelligent, amazing women – feel we must "look for" love, seek out and find it like some elusive unicorn in the forest that we could captivate and capture if only we were younger, prettier, blonder, thinner, smarter – or just rich and famous.

And yet how liberating, how exhilarating it is when we finally realize that the love we so desire is already ours. Not given when we're good enough, but ours just as we are. Love is always and forever our gift from the goddess, the Aphrodite inside.

Releasing Aphrodite began as a personal exploration of love, but soon evolved into book form as I became fascinated with – and wanted to share – a simple, beautiful, and very ancient way each of us can more fully feel the sensuous pleasures of loving life, ourselves and others using the pure fragrances of essential oils as aphrodisiacs.

Considered an integral part of the ritual and art of lovemaking since antiquity in the West, and for thousands of years before this in the East, these exquisite and powerfully persuasive scents may still be easily enjoyed by busy women of today to stimulate desire, arouse passion, and add romance and excitement to life and love.

Why hide our love away or save it for a rainy day? Why dole it out in small amounts on rare occasions only? Why not choose to love expansively, exuberantly, like the great goddess Aphrodite? Why not start today?

I hope you enjoy *Releasing Aphrodite*, and experiencing the many pleasures of being a woman who is free to love!

Warm wishes,

Elisabeth

Table of Contents

The Goddess Aphrodite

Ancient Gods and Goddesses

From the love affair between the Earth and Sky, the ancient Greeks believed great gods and goddesses were born, immortal though in human form. Invincible, inscrutable – supreme – these almighty forces ruled over life and death, the here and the hereafter, bringing harmony and chaos, good and evil to the vast stage of human existence.

Like characters in an unfolding drama, each god and goddess had a unique part to play in the story of creation. Worshipped and revered by mortal men and women who daily sought to please them, these mythic gods of old helped make the unknown understandable, the mysterious more real.

Of the twelve most powerful gods and goddesses, Zeus was the patriarch, the commander of the higher worlds, while Poseidon governed the sea and storms, and Hades, the subterranean territory of the dead. There was Artemis, goddess of the fields and forests; Athena, wise guardian of the city; Ares, dreaded god of war; and the beautiful Apollo, god of light and truth.

There was Hera, venerated wife and Zeus' queen; Hestia, goddess of the hearth and home; Hermes, god of the marketplace; and Haphaestus, master craftsman to the gods.

But fairest of them all, there was Aphrodite – the golden goddess of love, whose memory still lingers in the legends of today.

Aphrodite – Goddess of Love

The perfection of feminine loveliness, the embodiment of womanly love, Aphrodite arose fully grown from the warm, white foam of the Cyprian sea. Found floating naked on the waves, she was dressed by the Three Graces in opulent robes, adorned with precious jewels, and carried by the West Wind to Olympus, heavenly dwelling of the gods. And here, under a cloudless firmament of sunshine, even the gods succumbed to Aphrodite's charms, and shared with her the many pleasures of love in Paradise.

But not content to give herself only to the Gods, Aphrodite chose to also bring her love to Earth's green and flourishing land. Sometimes accompanied by Eros, the irresistible god of passion and desire, Aphrodite walked among ordinary men and women in various disguises. Silently or with cymbals clashing, by surprise or as an answered prayer, in daylight, in darkness and in dreams, she came to Earth to inspire and encourage love, and to leave behind her seed – the gift of the goddess that is love.

The Aphrodite Inside

Aphrodite's legacy, the capacity to love, exists in every woman like some elemental fire, some primal energy. The source of her power and her passion, her beauty and her warmth, her goodness and generosity, love is innate and inseparably hers to nurture, to celebrate and to share.

Since antiquity and perhaps always, a wide assortment of aphrodisiacs have been used by the wise and loving woman to facilitate the life-long process – and the fun – of increasing and releasing the love inside. Yet of all the exotic drinks and brews, of all the arousing foods and spices, of all the magic potions created throughout time, the woman knew the surest aphrodisiac of all was scent, and used the pure extracts of natural fragrance – the essential oils of aromatic plants and trees – freely, even lavishly, to assist her in the goddess work of love.

The ancient art of using essential oils as aphrodisiacs can still be easily enjoyed by the woman of today who chooses to not let her love stay dormant and unused, but to nourish it and help it grow – more for her, and more for others… and then to set it free.

Releasing the Aphrodite Inside
with Fragrances for Love

Fragrance – Nature's Aphrodisiac

In swaying fields of lavender, in secret groves of sweet-smelling orange blossoms, in moonlit gardens heavy with the scent of jasmine, the fragrances of Nature cast a spell so irresistibly enticing, so effortlessly inhaled.

More quickly than an arrow shot from Cupid's bow, fragrance travels through the sense of smell to that portion of the brain responsible for all emotion, imagination and memory, all instincts and intuition, all functions of survival including sexuality, and touches deep inside where love lives, to gently stir desire.

Capturing the Allure of Scent

Fragrance in the atmosphere originates in aromatic plants and trees as droplets of a highly volatile oil, called the essence of the plant. Located throughout the petals of a flower, the surface of a leaf, the rind of a fruit, the roots, resin or heartwood of a tree, these essential oils release their scent when warmed by the sun.

For millennia in the West and for thousands of years before

this in the East, numerous techniques have been developed to extract essential oils from their hidden recesses within the plant, and thus capture fleeting fragrance as a light and lovely oil, available for the enjoyment and enrichment of all.

The Ancient Art of Using Essential Oils as Aphrodisiacs

Used as aphrodisiacs by the Pharaohs of Egypt, the Emperors of Rome and the rulers of Greece, essential oils were regarded as precious gifts from the gods, and often considered more valuable than gold. Extensively studied by the ancient cultures more than 6,000 years ago, each essential oil was found to have an individual profile of effects on the body, mind and emotions, and a unique potential to aid love as an aphrodisiac.

For the woman of antiquity, essential oils were regarded as treasured resources in the ritual and art of making love. Luxuriating in a sensuous world of scent, the woman fragranced her bath with lavender, combed cedarwood through her hair and beautified her face with frankincense. She perfumed her body to entice him with rose oil on her lips, ylang ylang on her breasts and sandalwood on her thighs. And always, she set the scene for love, fragrancing her home with scents selected to serve her special needs and desires.

For every wish, the woman found a fragrant way to nurture love and help it grow, to heighten and sustain it, or simply to give thanks for love – and thoroughly enjoy it.

Releasing Aphrodite with Fragrances for Love

Like the woman of antiquity, like a wise enchantress in tales of old, the woman of today – the modern Aphrodite – can still enjoy the ancient art of using essential oils as aphrodisiacs to help her make wishes come true… or discover the thrill of something totally new!

Filled with simple, beautiful essential oil recipes for room fragrances, scented body lotions, sensual massages and aromatic baths, *Releasing Aphrodite* offers even the busiest woman, an easy and effective way to feel more sensuous and sexy, more carefree and confident, more irresistible, unforgettable and utterly irreplaceable… to feel free to love, like the great goddess Aphrodite.

Getting Ready for Love

Before loving another and experiencing the many joys of romantic and erotic love, the modern Aphrodite knows it's wise and wonderful to focus first on feeling good about herself, and taking pleasure in her life.

Like a flower that blossoms with tender care and nurturing, the modern Aphrodite sets aside some private time to nourish the love inside with quiet contemplation or more lively play. Striving to be gentle and generous with herself, she moves through her day with optimism and confidence, welcoming the new, yet always aware of the beauty in the present.

Opening her arms to life, the woman embraces the loveliness that surrounds her: the kaleidoscope of colors in the sky; the intricate melodies of birdsong; the warm softness of the breeze; the juicy flesh of summer fruit; and the sweet and spicy scents of life.

Happily secure in the quantity and quality of love she has to give, the modern Aphrodite is ready to share her love with others, and feel the joys of love returned a hundred-fold (plus interest).

The following essential oil recipes for room fragrances, scented body lotions and aromatic baths are designed to stir that loving feeling, and help every woman remember she's fabulous and fascinating, high-spirited and sensuous… and pretty hot stuff!

So, give yourself a moment, even on the busiest day, to luxuriate in a personal pleasure dome of scents wafting through the air. Or before a special evening out, perfume your body with confidence-boosting lotions to help you enter any room smiling – and ready to say yes to joy, to love, to life.

Smile (and see him smile back at you)!

Room Fragrances *to Prepare a Woman for Love*

Superbly Alive

To feel vibrant and vivacious, full of life – awake, aware, and wonderfully well...

Sheer Bliss

...sprinkle in an oil burner

Geranium	2 drops
Mandarin	3 drops
Orange	3 drops

This sunny, blue-sky summertime scent sparkles with positive energy, and helps a woman more fully know the untamed thrill, the sheer bliss of being alive.

Say Yes

...sprinkle in an oil burner

Cedarwood	3 drops
Patchouli	2 drops
Rose	2 drops

Like a temptress saint, the fragrance of cedarwood, patchouli and rose excites the physical passion and the spiritual power to say yes to life!

Set Free

To be liberated from fears and inhibitions, and set free – free at last – to love, unreservedly…

Fearless

…sprinkle in an oil burner

Juniper	3 drops
Rosemary	3 drops

An empowering, exhilarating fragrance in the air, this blend builds a woman's desire and determination to cast away her cares, and simply seize the day.

Flying High

...sprinkle in an oil burner

Bergamot	4 drops
Clary Sage	1 drop
Frankincense	3 drops

When the heart is willing but shyness blocks the way, the elevating, slightly intoxicating combination of these scents increases a woman's confidence to spread her wings and fly!

Looking Good

To remember, even on the off-days, to enjoy the special beauty that is every woman's gift, and to smile and strut her stuff a little – just for the fun of it...

Absolutely Fabulous

...sprinkle in an oil burner

Mandarin	2 drops
Orange	2 drops
Jasmine	1 drop
Neroli	2 drops

A luscious fragrance of fruit and florals, this scent stimulates a carefree sensuality, and makes a woman feel absolutely fabulous – flaws and all!

Simply Gorgeous

...sprinkle in an oil burner

Jasmine	1 drop
Rose	2 drops
Bergamot	4 drops

These stunningly beautiful, star-studded scents leave a girl feeling glamorous and sexy, and simply gorgeous too!

Like A Goddess

To experience the power and the pleasure of being a woman who, like the great goddess Aphrodite, knows that love is hers and life awaits…

Mighty Aphrodite

…sprinkle in an oil burner

Cedarwood	3 drops
Jasmine	1 drop

This fragrance in the air strengthens a woman's natural ability to make things happen – and turn a head or two.

Cupid's Arrow

...sprinkle in an oil burner

Rose	2 drops
Sandalwood	4 drops

Like Cupid with his arrow, the fragrance of rose and sandalwood gives a woman the confidence to always hit her target. Just aim... and fire!

High-Spirited

To let the spirits soar and get into a mood for play and laughter, with perhaps a bit of loving after...

Oh Disobey!

...sprinkle in an oil burner

Pine	2 drops
Orange	4 drops

A fragrance that teases: oh disobey, the cheerful carefree scents of pine and orange invite a youthful rebellion to break the rules – and just go out to play!

Go Astray

...sprinkle in an oil burner

Patchouli	1 drop
Sandalwood	2 drops
Clary Sage	1 drop
Mandarin	4 drops

This wayward fragrance wafting through the air leads a girl astray, and entices her to enjoy the naughty pleasures of misbehaving for a day.

All Systems Go

To rev up the system till it's raring to go, feeling energized, enthusiastic and eager for action…

Engines Running

…sprinkle in an oil burner

Pine	3 drops
Rosemary	3 drops

A marvellously invigorating blend, these fragrances stimulate energy and start those engines running.

Ready, Set...

...sprinkle in an oil burner

Black Pepper	2 drops
Clove	2 drops
Orange	4 drops

The high voltage scent of black pepper, clove and orange in a room switch on the physical, the sensual, the powerful urge to love every day. Ready, set... go!

Scented Body Lotions *for Boosting Confidence*

Enter Smiling

To enter any social scene calm and composed, self-assured and smiling…

Crushed Cedarwood

…combine

Cedarwood	3 drops
Unperfumed body lotion	1 tbsp

The rich, warm fragrance distilled from the wood of the ancient cedarwood tree is soothing and centering, and builds a woman's quiet confidence, just to be herself.

Juniper Berry Balsam

...combine

Juniper	4 drops
Unperfumed body lotion	1 tbsp

Before even the most challenging social event, this balsamic-scented body lotion reminds a woman she's bigger – and braver – than her fears.

Sweet Geranium

...combine

| Geranium | 3 drops |
| Unperfumed body lotion | 1 tbsp |

Like a freshly picked posy of flowers, the sweetly floral, feminine fragrance of geranium lifts the spirits for fun, and strengthens a woman's confidence to go for it... and see what comes!

Rosemary Herbal

...combine

| Rosemary | 4 drops |
| Unperfumed body lotion | 1 tbsp |

A real knock-out of a body lotion, the invigorating herbal scent of rosemary on the skin makes a girl feel fighting fit, and guarantees she'll make it to the final round – smiling and victorious!

Aromatic Baths – *Purely for the Pleasure*

Stolen Moments

To steal away and luxuriate in the fragrant waters of a bath, and finally to emerge from this sea of scents feeling womanly and sensuous – and a little saucy, too...

Stillness and Serenity

...sprinkle in a full bath

Chamomile	1 drop
Lavender	3 drops
Frankincense	2 drops

As calm and tranquil as a quiet stream, these super-relaxing scents create a sense of stillness and serenity.

Someone Special

...sprinkle in a full bath

Neroli	2 drops
Rose	2 drops
Ylang Ylang	2 drops

A long, leisurely soak in this exquisite floral-scented bath is a totally pampering and pleasurable experience for someone special – you.

Shockingly Sensuous

...sprinkle in a full bath

Clary Sage	2 drops
Patchouli	2 drops
Ylang Ylang	2 drops

This rather risqué combination of scents sneaks up on a woman and whisks her away to some shockingly sensuous places.

So Saucy

...sprinkle in a full bath

Geranium	2 drops
Rosemary	2 drops
Orange	4 drops

With a wink and a whistle, these light-hearted scents get a girl feeling playful, spontaneous, and ever-so-saucy!

Stimulating Desire

The allure of Aphrodite – a light so mesmerizing and magnetic – exists in every woman who chooses to shine her love on others. For this modern Aphrodite, there is no need to wait or wish for love. She knows that love will come to her if she desires just to give it.

Every day, in many ways, not always serious but also playful and spontaneous, the modern Aphrodite wants to offer others the gifts of her affection and attention, her humor and generosity, her sheer exuberance for living.

From friendly flirtations to more intimate encounters, she wants to amuse, delight, beguile; to charm, enchant and captivate others with the power of her love. A love that, like a force of nature, draws the love of others to her, the woman wants to tempt and tease; to tantalize and fascinate; to entice, incite, ignite the red hot sparks of passion.

Sure of her desires, this daughter of the goddess smiles with anticipation: love is the greatest aphrodisiac – and she intends to use it!

The following essential oil recipes for room fragrances, scented body lotions and aromatic baths are designed to increase every woman's desire to love, and to stimulate through the provocative powers of scent, some not-so-innocent flirtations, as well as more seriously sexy seductions.

Why not curl up on the sofa with a room fragrance to excite your favorite fantasies, or enjoy a bit of naughty water-play in a fragrant bath for two. The day, and night, are yours: choose to desire… and see how irresistibly desirable you become.

Dare to desire!

Room Fragrances *to Ignite the Sparks of Passion*

Secrets and Fantasies

To remember what was (and what could be again), or imagine what would be (if daydreams came true), to let the mind roam in that most erogenous zone…

Outlaw

…sprinkle in an oil burner

Clove	2 drops
Patchouli	2 drops
Bergamot	4 drops

The rebel, the cowboy, the outlaw, the rogue, the thrill of the chase and the triumph of conquest – this room fragrance is all about him: dangerously sexy and unlawfully hot. An almost illegally sensual scent, clove, patchouli and bergamot set free the outlaw inside.

007

...sprinkle in an oil burner

Black Pepper	2 drops
Rosemary	2 drops
Sandalwood	2 drops
Bergamot	2 drops

Filled with high-speed adventure and non-stop excitement, the debonair, dashing scent of 007 sweeps a girl off her feet and takes her away from it all for a while.

Sailor Boy

...sprinkle in an oil burner

Pine	2 drops
Sandalwood	4 drops

Like a sailor on shore leave looking for love, pine and sandalwood exude a crisply controlled, well-contained masculinity with something wonderfully wild lurking beneath. A beautiful, hungry sailor-boy scent, this (un)gentlemanly combination calls a woman out for the hunt.

First Sight

…sprinkle in an oil burner

Vetivert	1 drop
Cedarwood	2 drops
Frankincense	3 drops

The combustible, charismatic scent of vetivert, cedarwood and frankincense stimulates a desire for love at first sight – love that needs only a look to ignite.

Not-so-Innocent Flirtations

To increase the suspense between the said and the unsaid – the revealed and the hidden – and to use the evocative language of scent to ask someone special in the room…

Sugar or Spice?

…sprinkle in an oil burner

Rose	1 drop
Clove	2 drops
Mandarin	3 drops

So very feminine but sexy too, this beguiling room fragrance arouses his curiosity and draws him closer with the sweet temptation of a woman who is both naughty and nice, and promises treats – sugar or spice?

Feel the Heat?

...sprinkle in an oil burner

Geranium	2 drops
Orange	3 drops
Black Pepper	1 drop

The combination of geranium, orange and black pepper is both friendly and flirtatious. Outgoing and vivacious on the surface, yet shimmering with innuendo underneath, these fragrances create an aura of intrigue, as fascinating as the woman who plays with fire... does he feel the heat?

Can He Catch Her?

...sprinkle in an oil burner

Mandarin	3 drops
Orange	3 drops
Ylang Ylang	2 drops

A sunny, youthful scent that's full of mischief, the fresh and saucy fragrance of mandarin, orange and ylang ylang in a room offers a clear but playful challenge. Can he catch this sassie lassie?

Does He Dare?

...sprinkle in an oil burner

Rose	2 drops
Neroli	2 drops

A near perfect fragrance of femininity and grace, rose and neroli pose a tantalizing dilemma for any man: dare he approach her? (Oh do!)

Seriously Sexy Seductions

To capture his attention, to startle and take his breathe away, to heighten his anticipation that soon his dreams will all come true…

Whisper

…sprinkle in an oil burner

Lavender	4 drops
Neroli	2 drops

Intimate and warm, like her breath on his neck, these softly sensuous scents whisper: come closer, closer still.

Why Not?

...sprinkle in an oil burner

Geranium	2 drops
Mandarin	4 drops
Clary Sage	2 drops

A fragrance full of fun and frank flirtation, this room fragrance sets his fantasies in motion and gets him thinking: hey, why not? And here? And now? How nice!

Wolf Whistle

...sprinkle in an oil burner

Clove	1 drop
Ylang Ylang	1 drop
Bergamot	3 drops

The ebony, exotic scent of clove, ylang ylang and bergamot exudes an almost dangerous allure. A fragrance to make pussycats growl and grown men whimper, this frightfully seductive blend gives the wolf a whistle.

Wild at Heart

...sprinkle in an oil burner

Patchouli	2 drops
Bergamot	2 drops
Orange	2 drops

*Animal, physical, earthy and erotic,
the provocative scent of patchouli,
bergamot and orange tempts him with
a thrilling proposition: let's go native
and be wild at heart.*

Scented Body Lotions *for Seduction*

Passion Flowers

To use the pure fragrances of Nature's greatest floral aphrodisiacs to stimulate desire and set alight the fire of passionate love…

Alluring Rose

…combine

Rose	3 drops
Unperfumed body lotion	1 tbsp

Like the scent of Aphrodite, the perfect beauty and flawless femininity of rose in this body lotion is magnetically alluring.

Romantic Neroli

...combine

Neroli	3 drops
Unperfumed body lotion	1 tbsp

The courtly, Camelot scent of neroli entices any man with scented promises of stolen kisses beneath the delicate orange blossom tree.

Seductive Ylang Ylang

...combine

Ylang Ylang	4 drops
Unperfumed body lotion	1 tbsp

Evocative as a lush island paradise, the South Seas scent of ylang ylang exudes the innocent seductivity of barefoot island maidens who sing a siren's song.

Irresistible Jasmine

...combine

Jasmine	3 drops
Unperfumed body lotion	1 tbsp

Like a secret rendezvous, the simply irresistible scent of jasmine in this body lotion quickens the heart in anticipation of soon being together again.

Aromatic Baths *for Two*

Water Play

To enjoy a bit of good clean fun in a fragrant bath for two, and then to slowly start to play a more grown-up game or two...

Up to Mischief

...sprinkle in a full bath

Sandalwood	3 drops
Orange	3 drops

A sure-fire way to start trouble, a bath with these seductive scents inspires a youthful, lusty carefreeness that's spontaneous... and very mischievous.

Making Whoopie!

...sprinkle in a full bath

Rosemary	2 drops
Mandarin	4 drops

A wow of a scent, exuberant and energetic, the combination of rosemary and mandarin gets couples in the mood for making whoopie. Whoopie for love!

Steamy Water

...sprinkle in a full bath

Black Pepper	2 drops
Cedarwood	3 drops

Lovers beware: the sultry, exotic scents of black pepper and cedarwood quickly turn the atmosphere to steamy, and the temperature to hot!

Swept Away

...sprinkle in a full bath

Patchouli	1 drop
Ylang Ylang	2 drops
Bergamot	3 drops

Like a tidal wave or a great storm at sea, this powerfully erotic combination sweeps lovers away.

Enjoying *Eros*

*For the modern Aphrodite who wishes
to more thoroughly enjoy erotic love,
no manuals are required, no textbooks
of technique. Simply the willingness to
surrender – to let go and give in to the
supremely sensuous pleasures of sexual
love with him.*

Her man – sometimes unfathomable, yet always fascinating – the modern Aphrodite loves her chosen mate like earth loves rain: naturally, simply, soaking him up. Drawing him closer with the force of her desire, she invites him with a smile to join her in a dance that only lovers do.

With her concentration focused solely on sensation, she feels the warm dampness of his flesh. She hears his breathing, rhythmic and insistent. She tastes his kisses and catches the scent of him. Transformed before her eyes by the tension of desire into her Eros – her opposite but equal partner in a perfectly-matched dance of love.

Spellbound by the magic, liquified by love, the modern Aphrodite now rests contentedly in the golden warmth of the afterglow. She has savored the joys of surrender – and wants to dance (lots more) with him.

The following essential oil recipes for room fragrances, scented body rubs and aromatic baths are designed to create many melodies for love – some orchestrated by angels, others deliciously devilish – and entice lovers to dance not only to old favorites but to find in unexpected beats and unusual harmonies, some heart-stoppingly marvellous new tunes.

Tonight, light the candles and turn on the music with bedroom scents more sexy than Sinatra, or start the fun with a body rub that gets him – and you – in the mood for love.

Dance with him today!

Room Fragrances *to Increase Enjoyment of Erotic Love*

Classical Harmony

To create an atmosphere of lyrical beauty and harmony in which there is time to gaze into the ocean of his eyes, and to slowly inspire a symphony of feeling, at once expected yet always new…

Moonlight Serenade

…sprinkle in an oil burner

Neroli	2 drops
Lavender	2 drops
Bergamot	3 drops
Vetivert	1 drop

A fragrance of classical beauty – tranquil and serene – this essence in the air evokes a languorous, velvety sensuality, with just a touch of the gloriously shocking, like Eros sliding in beside her.

Mahler's Fifth

...sprinkle in an oil burner

Jasmine	1 drop
Sandalwood	2 drops
Bergamot	4 drops

Symphonic, stirring and flushed with passion, these scents unsettle couples nestled in the security of daily routines, and stimulate their desire to explore love's more exotic places.

Only Rock 'n' Roll

To get into a party mood that is playful, provocative and explicitly physical, and to feel moved by a beat so exuberantly alive – arms held high and hips swaying...

(Can't Get No) Satisfaction

...sprinkle in an oil burner

Clove	2 drops
Mandarin	4 drops

A steamy, sexy jungle scent – full of drumbeat, full of fun – clove and mandarin leave him breathless and smiling, after a night of rock 'n' roll.

Get Down Tonight

...sprinkle in an oil burner

Patchouli	1 drop
Pine	2 drops
Orange	4 drops

For an unconventional, uninhibited musical experience, the powerfully masculine scent of patchouli, pine and orange pumps up the volume... and gets down to basics.

All That Jazz

To prolong the exquisite pleasure of heightened expectation through all those syncopated rhythms, riffs and refrains with style, stamina, intelligence and humor...

Fly Me to the Moon

...sprinkle in an oil burner

Jasmine	1 drop
Clary Sage	1 drop
Black Pepper	2 drops
Bergamot	3 drops

An intoxicating, sultry, night-time scent, this combustible combination gives lovers strength to let their fires burn more slowly, until both are caught up in the flames.

Let's Face the Music and Dance

...sprinkle in an oil burner

Rosemary	2 drops
Mandarin	2 drops
Orange	2 drops

A jubilee of scent, these uplifting, energizing fragrances in a room provide a light and tinkling melody that makes a couple want to dance, and sing... sing... sing.

Salsa, Baby!

To perform an exhilarating dance of passion, coordinated by experts who have mastered the art of sensual concentration, plus some pretty fancy footwork…

Amor Divino

…sprinkle in an oil burner

Jasmine	2 drops
Clove	2 drops
Orange	4 drops

For a virtuoso display of sexual prowess, these electric, incendiary scents free up the mind to stop thinking, and focus on feeling instead.

(More Than) Un Poquito Más

...sprinkle in an oil burner

Neroli	2 drops
Patchouli	2 drops
Ylang Ylang	2 drops

This is a bold scent, like panthers stalking. A graceful, sleek fragrance for when two mighty forces meet in a collision most tender, this blend provokes an animal magnetism and an uninhibited eroticism.

Soul Sounds

To start perhaps as strangers or estranged, and then be slowly drawn together, enthralled by the hypnotic, pulsating sounds of love and longing – to connect in a dance so sexy, so sensational, so unforgettable...

In the Midnight Hour

...sprinkle in an oil burner

Ylang Ylang	2 drops
Jasmine	1 drop
Bergamot	3 drops

A moonlight blend, this fragrance is both innocent and erotic, like love that suddenly erupts between two souls bedazzled by the night.

Everlasting Love

...sprinkle in an oil burner

Vetivert	1 drop
Rose	2 drops
Orange	3 drops

The divine scent of vetivert, rose and orange takes lovers on a journey from poignant yearning to joyful release and final finger-snapping, foot-stomping gratitude: oh gods of love, we thank you!

Fragrant Body Rubs *From Back…to Front*

Four Stages of Pleasure

To slowly anoint him with fragrant oil, gently stroking the shape of his body, feeling the heat of him, and sharing the pleasures of awakening love…

Stage I

…combine

Sweet almond oil	1 tbsp
Lavender	2 drops

Tenderly rub this silky smooth body lotion along the length of his back, over his shoulders and down again, over and over until he's eased of all tension, and then…

Stage II

...add to the previous blend

Sandalwood   2 drops

Sprinkle two drops of sandalwood in the blend, and repeatedly sweep the mixture over his buttocks, slipping down to the back of his thighs, moving up the sensitive sides, and starting all over again and again, until he's breathless with anticipation, and then...

Stage III

...add to the previous blend

Ylang Ylang   1 drop

Adding one drop of ylang ylang into the blend, now roll him over onto his back, massaging each fingertip, then stroking his hands, moving up to his arms and caressing his chest, until his heart is beating almost too hard, and then...

Stage IV

...add to the previous blend

Patchouli   1 drop

Release him at last with a drop of patchouli, gently massaging his stomach, around and around, then moving down to his hips and beyond, until his pleasure (and yours) is (almost) complete.

Aromatic Baths *in the Afterglow*

Intimate Celebrations

To prolong the intimacy of being close in ways that only lovers can, to linger over memories of love, and just smile, smile, smile…

Sea of Flowers

…sprinkle in a full bath

Rose	2 drops
Ylang Ylang	2 drops

Floating in this sea of flowers, drifting slowly, half asleep, this gorgeous bath blend is a special treat… reserved for lovers only.

Sweet Talk

...sprinkle in a full bath

Chamomile	3 drops
Neroli	2 drops

These quiet, soothing scents induce a sense of calm contentment, in which sweet words of love are spoken softly in the golden moments of the afterglow.

Shipwrecked

...sprinkle in a full bath

Ylang Ylang	2 drops
Rosemary	1 drop
Bergamot	3 drops

Shipwrecked on the shores of love, the gently stimulating scents of ylang ylang, rosemary and bergamot restore a couple's energy after rigorous exertion... and ready them for more.

All Smiles

...sprinkle in a full bath

| Geranium | 2 drops |
| Orange | 3 drops |

A cheerful, bubbly blend of scents, like sparkling pink champagne, this bath is for lovers who want to celebrate: ain't we great!

Living As Lovers

The pleasure of sharing a love that's true – a love that changes but never fades – can be enjoyed by every woman who makes a promise and a passionate commitment to love her mate, not in return or as reward, but to love first for its own sake, as she would wish to be loved by him.

True to herself and truly herself with him, the modern Aphrodite freely reveals not only the events and experiences of her day, but also her most intimate thoughts and feelings, her hopes and dreams, as part of an ongoing and evolving process of uncovering and discovering herself with him.

Her most beloved mate, a man so familiar yet still a mystery, the woman knows he is an original, unique individual, and generously assists him in fulfilling his destiny. United and connected in the safety of each other's arms, she holds him close and sets him free to stand or soar, to rest or grow, to be all he is, and all he wishes to be.

With tenderness and truthfulness, with light-heartedness and humor, the modern Aphrodite promises to give her best to love. And here, in truly loving, she happily awaits the exquisite pleasures of true love showered on her every day, like rose petals from the sky.

The following essential oil recipes for room fragrances, scented body rubs and aromatic baths are designed to help couples live as lovers, and inspire and enhance those precious moments of intimacy at home with him.

Today, help love flourish with a fragrance to fill any room, at any time, with scents that encourage a sense of connection and a natural sensuality …or just knock his socks off with a fragrant surprise or two.

Make a promise – and say you do!

Room Fragrances *to Inspire Intimacy With Him*

Love in the Living Room
To savor the closeness and contentment of love that's tried and true, yet to also keep alive the wide-eyed thrill of love that's new…

Sharing Time

…sprinkle in an oil burner

Chamomile	1 drop
Lavender	3 drops
Bergamot	3 drops

The easy intimacy of this fragrance flowing through the air inspires lovers to enjoy the simple pleasures of just sharing time – and doing nothing special for a night.

Lazy Sundays

...sprinkle in an oil burner

Ylang Ylang	2 drops
Orange	6 drops

A soft voluptuous scent for lovers, the combination of ylang ylang and orange is ideal for lazy Sundays that should never end, with lots of time to slouch about and yawn and stretch, bare limbs entangled.

Soft Music and Candlelight

...sprinkle in an oil burner

Rose	2 drops
Vetivert	1 drop

Like soft music and candlelight, these scents in a room create an irresistible aura of romance, in which to kiss and cuddle on the sofa.

Larking About

...sprinkle in an oil burner

Geranium	1 drop
Mandarin	4 drops
Rosemary	2 drops

This zany scent touches the funny bone and gets couples in a playful mood for larking about in the living room. Anyone for hide and seek?

Dinners for Two

To set the scene for a romantic meal together, with lots of lively conversation, plus a surprise or two…

Simple Suppers

…sprinkle in an oil burner

Orange	4 drops
Lavender	3 drops

The delectable blend of orange and lavender is the perfect recipe for relaxing and reconnecting over supper, and delighting in the simple things of life.

Special Occasions

...sprinkle in an oil burner

Clove	1 drop
Black Pepper	1 drop
Rose	1 drop
Bergamot	4 drops

These spicy fragrances heat up a room on those special occasions when dinner is a prelude to romance.

Surprise (# 1)

...sprinkle in an oil burner

Jasmine	1 drop
Black Pepper	1 drop
Bergamot	4 drops

When the invitation's for a black-tie dinner in the kitchen at eight, this racy fragrance makes sure he doesn't come late!

Surprise (# 2)

...sprinkle in an oil burner

Neroli	2 drops
Rose	1 drop
Mandarin	4 drops

Serve this scent with a meal-time surprise – you, all dressed for dinner in just a silky white robe and a string of pearls.

Behind the Bedroom Door

To put aside (if only for a while) the needs of others and, in the privacy of a sensuously pleasing space, to focus instead on the happiness of "us"…

Hideaway

…sprinkle in an oil burner

Geranium	1 drop
Neroli	2 drops
Lavender	3 drops

This fragrance in a bedroom evokes a mood of peacefulness, with just a hint of playfulness, for couples who want to spend some time alone in their private hideaway.

In Harmony

...sprinkle in an oil burner

Frankincense	3 drops
Juniper	3 drops

Like a safe harbor, the scent of frankincense and juniper create an atmosphere of calm conciliation in which a couple can navigate through rocky waters, and find their way to harmony again.

Hat Trick

...sprinkle in an oil burner

Rosemary	3 drops
Orange	4 drops
Rose	1 drop

Too tired for love? Too stressed for sex?
These stimulating, sexy scents in the air
act like a magic potion, and (presto!)
pull a (romantic) rabbit from the hat!

Us Two

...sprinkle in an oil burner

Rose   3 drops

The heavenly fragrance of rose offers a silent prayer in scent, and helps a couple strive each day to find joy in the smallest places, in hidden things, in being home together.

Scented Body Rubs *for Him and Her*

Lovers' Gifts

To massage each other with perfumed oils and attempt to discover which is the greater pleasure: to give or to receive...

She Gives Him – The Unexpected

...combine

Sandalwood	3 drops
Frankincense	3 drops
Sweet almond oil	1 tbsp

An exotic, intriguing scent, sandalwood and frankincense offer him the unexpected pleasure of discovering she's more daring than he ever dreamed.

He Gives Her – A Treat

...combine

Jasmine	1 drop
Ylang Ylang	2 drops
Sweet almond oil	1 tbsp

The ultimate luxury, this lavish massage oil is a treat just for her – a woman who deserves the best.

She Gives Him – Enduring Love

...combine

Cedarwood   3 drops
Sweet almond oil   1 tbsp

A symbol of her enduring love, the fragrance of cedarwood in this body rub promises him a partnership that's sure – signed, sealed and delivered daily with a kiss.

He Gives Her – His Love Forever

...combine

Rose	2 drops
Neroli	2 drops
Sweet almond oil	1 tbsp

For now and ever after, rose and neroli express in scent his silent pledge: I do love you.

Aromatic Baths *Before Bed*

To Sleep or Not to Sleep...?

To answer this often unasked question, and choose to be either soothed or stimulated before bedtime...

Nice and Cozy

...sprinkle in a full bath

Chamomile	1 drop
Lavender	4 drops

For a beautifully relaxing night-time bath, chamomile and lavender prepare a couple for the comforts of bed – all nice and cozy with only a good book between them.

Nite Nite

...sprinkle in a full bath

Frankincense	4 drops
Neroli	2 drops

A sedating elixir of scents, this bath blend washes away stresses and strains and, like a gently rocking cradle, helps a couple drift off to a deep and restful sleep. Nite, nite.

Not Yet

...sprinkle in a full bath

Clary Sage	2 drops
Sandalwood	4 drops

These arousing, sensuous scents in the bath stir the imagination for some sexy bedtime stories on those nights when a couple is ready for bed, but not yet ready for sleep.

Last Kiss

...sprinkle in a full bath

Rose	1 drop
Frankincense	2 drops
Bergamot	3 drops

A dreamy scent with bedroom eyes, bathing in these fragrances makes lovers want one more caress, one final embrace, one last kiss before goodnight.

Creating Personalized Love Potions
Choosing and Using Essential Oils for Love

While *Releasing Aphrodite* presents a wide range of exquisite essential oil recipes to suit many situations and evoke many moods, this section offers the busy modern woman basic tips on creating a personalized love potion to address her individual needs, fulfill her specific wishes, or just explore some as yet unsampled pleasures.

It's easy – and it's fun, simply:

- Decide how you'd like to use the essential oils – that is, as a room fragrance, in a body lotion, massage blend or added to a bath.

- Select one to three essential oils that cause the desired effects from the *Guide to Essential Oils for Love and Romance* that follows, or refer to the *Index* on page 159.

- If you wish, check to make sure the essential oils you've chosen blend well together using the table *Fragrance Categories and Complementary Scents* on page 151.

● Then follow these simple guidelines:

Using Essential Oils as a Room Fragrance
Sprinkle the recommended number of drops of the essential oils selected (see the table that accompanies each oil listed) in an oil burner, making sure the total number does not exceed eight drops.

Using Essential Oils on the Body
Sprinkle the recommended number of drops of the essential oils selected (see the table that accompanies each oil listed) in one tablespoon or roughly one palm-full of a commercially-available unscented body lotion or a vegetable oil, such as sweet almond oil, making sure the total number does not exceed six drops.

Using Essential Oils in the Bath
Sprinkle the recommended number of drops of the essential oils selected (see the table that accompanies each oil listed) in a full bath – a running bath speeds evaporation of the fragrances – making sure the total number does not exceed six drops.

If despite using the recommended number of drops, skin irritation or tingling develops, rub the affected area with sweet almond or olive oil; the reaction will subside usually within an hour.

Heed cautions where indicated, avoid contact with the eyes, and do not use the essential oils internally.

And finally, remember: although awareness of a scent will fade, the fragrance still continues to work its special magic. Just perfume a room, a body lotion, a massage blend or a bath with your personalized love potion – and enjoy what happens next!

Guide to Essential Oils for Love and Romance

This guide describes the individual characteristics of 21 beautiful and evocative essential oils, including their primary effects and suggested uses for pleasure. Whether the invigorating scent of rosemary for added energy, the enticing scent of jasmine for excitement, or the fairytale fragrance of neroli for romance, the diversity of the following essential oils offers every woman a wide selection of scents to help her make love more stimulating and satisfying, more fulfilling and more fun!

Essential Oil	Description
Bergamot	Classically Beautiful
Black Pepper	Intriguing and Exciting
Cedarwood	Fortifying
Chamomile	Calming and Comforting
Clary Sage	Intoxicating
Clove	Spicy, Sultry and Very Hot
Frankincense	Inspiring
Geranium	Feminine and Full of Fun
Jasmine	Irresistible
Juniper	Elevating and Liberating
Lavender	Soothing and Stabilizing
Mandarin	Simply Delightful
Neroli	Romantic
Orange	Refreshing and Reviving
Patchouli	Provocative and Passionate
Pine	Invigorating
Rose	Effortlessly Seductive
Rosemary	Strengthening and Stimulating
Sandalwood	Sensational
Vetivert	Fascinating and Unforgettable
Ylang Ylang	Hypnotizing

Classically Beautiful

Bergamot

Profile

Born in the warm air of the Eastern Mediterranean, the small and dainty bergamot tree is one of nature's most delightful creations. Brought to Europe by Christopher Columbus who discovered it growing in the Canary Islands, the tree has lush green leaves, fragrant white flowers and pear-shaped fruit with a thin yellow rind from which the essential oil is extracted. A light-hearted citrus scent with a suggestion of soft florals and a slightly spicy undertone, bergamot has been used since at least the 16th century as a key ingredient in many fine perfumes, including the classic eau de cologne.

Uplifting and enlivening, the essential oil of bergamot coaxes and charms away stress and sadness, and gently eases the flow of spontaneity and sensuality. For those who are inhibited by insecurity or shyness, or who fear the force of their own emotions, the scent of bergamot helps promote the confidence and composure to seek love, feel love, show love.

• Elevates mood • Builds confidence • Encourages spontaneity

Suggestions for Pleasure

The classically beautiful scent of bergamot makes a lively room fragrance to lighten the atmosphere and lift the mood

Bergamot

Uses	Maximum Drops
Room fragrance	4 in oil burner
Bath oil	3 in full bath
Body lotion	3 in 1 tbsp unscented body lotion
Massage blend	3 in 1 tbsp sweet almond oil

May cause photosensitivity;
avoid before exposure to the sun or ultraviolet light.

in readiness for fun. Before a romantic evening, a quiet bath with bergamot is reviving and refreshing – or just add a drop of jasmine to stir more than a hint of passion.

Intriguing and Exciting

Black Pepper

Profile

Black pepper has been used as a stimulant in the East for over 4,000 years and was recommended by the Romans to strengthen male sexual performance. Not surprisingly, the fragrance obtained from the still unripe berries of the vine-like pepper plant was a favorite among the Egyptians, Greeks and especially the Romans, for whom the scent evoked the earthy sensuality they sought. Often valued more highly than gold, tributes, taxes and even the ransom of Rome were paid in pepper, while its trade opened up the great routes East.

Dark, dusky and mysterious, the penetrating spicy scent distilled from the dried, still unripe berries of the pepper plant exudes intrigue and romance. Said to be ruled by Mars, the fragrance promotes stamina, increases mental alertness and concentration, builds the will and the courage to act, expands the imagination, and satisfies that nameless hunger – the essence of erotica. For lovers who wish to banish lethargy

● Stimulates energy ● Increases desire

and indifference, particularly when due to hidden frustrations and anger, the alluring, enigmatic, daring scent of pepper rekindles the fire of passionate love.

Black Pepper

Uses	Maximum Drops
Room fragrance	3 in oil burner
Bath oil	2 in full bath
Body lotion	3 in 1 tbsp unscented body lotion
Massage blend	3 in 1 tbsp sweet almond oil

Suggestions for Pleasure

Renowned since antiquity as a strengthener and stimulant, black pepper is wonderful in massage blends to increase energy before arduous activity, or to restore it after!

Fortifying

Cedarwood

Profile

The ancient Syrians and Mesopotamians nourished the spirits of their ancestors with the incense of cedarwood and considered it a sign of continuity and enduring love. Once grown in the vast "holy forests" of Lebanon, where for centuries men found solace amidst the majestic cedarwoods, the tree may live for thousands of years, apparently immune to time, evergreen and fragrant.

The Egyptians believed cedarwood was imperishable and used its hard reddish wood as building material for palaces and temples, ships and sarcophagi, while its high content of balsamic oil was widely employed in all areas of daily life, from medicines to perfumes. So enormous were the quantities consumed that the tree's native habitat in the land of Canaan was conquered by the Egyptians to ensure a sufficient supply of the precious cedarwood tree.

● Relaxes mind and body ● Builds confidence ● Fortifies commitment

The woody, sensuously pleasing scent of cedarwood inspires a quiet strength and an inner calm and confidence. Particularly

---

Cedarwood

Uses	Maximum Drops
Room fragrance	3 in oil burner
Bath oil	3 in full bath
Body lotion	3 in 1 tbsp unscented body lotion
Massage blend	3 in 1 tbsp sweet almond oil

Avoid during pregnancy.

---

in times of turmoil, the fragrance of cedarwood helps fortify a couple's commitment to remain faithful to love.

Suggestions for Pleasure

The rich woody scent of cedarwood helps relax an over-intellectualized mind, and thus makes an excellent room fragrance to soothe away stress after a hectic day.

Calming and Comforting

Chamomile

Profile

Renowned for thousands of years as a natural healer, chamomile was considered a sacred plant by the ancient Egyptians who dedicated it to their sun god, Ra. The fresh and fruity fragrance – like red apples, round and ripening – distilled from chamomile's daisy-like white flowers is similarly regarded as one of the gentlest and most healing essential oils.

With a scent as comforting as a lover's soft caress, chamomile excels at calming anger and anxiety, particularly in those who find it difficult to relax and let go, who over-work and out-perform, but often end exhausted, irritable and discontented. As a reassuring support to couples going through a difficult time, the fragrance of chamomile helps foster an ability to listen with compassion, to speak with sensitivity, and to seek with diligence a loving resolution.

● Relaxes mind and body ● Fortifies commitment

Suggestions for Pleasure

The summertime scent of chamomile reduces irritability and tension, and when sprinkled in a bath for two reminds lovers to see the sunny side of life.

Chamomile

Uses	Maximum Drops
Room fragrance	3 in oil burner
Bath oil	3 in full bath
Body lotion	3 in 1 tbsp unscented body lotion
Massage blend	3 in 1 tbsp sweet almond oil

Intoxicating

Clary Sage

Profile

Clary sage has been used in Europe since the 16th century as an additive in beer and wine, and indeed the fragrance distilled from its purplish flowers and heart-shaped leaves has an intoxicating effect. At first relaxing then reviving, the scent of clary sage decreases shyness and inhibitions and increases a sense of elation, even euphoria.

Like an earthy seductress, the sensual, slightly musky scent of clary sage is full of possibilities. When the stress of daily life weighs heavily, clary sage awakens a powerful desire to overthrow constraints and set the spirit free. For lovers who feel restricted by demands or conventions, for lovers whose passion has grown stale or subdued, for lovers who wish to explore the unforeseen together – for these lovers, the fragrance of clary sage is a liberating aphrodisiac. A favorite ingredient in white magic potions, clary sage helps a couple abandon the rules and make fantasies real.

● Excites imagination ● Decreases inhibitions ● Increases desire

Suggestions for Pleasure

When used as a room fragrance, especially if combined with a few drops of orange, the arousing scent of clary sage helps a woman feel gloriously high on life, and ready to love.

Clary Sage

Uses	Maximum Drops
Room fragrance	2 in oil burner
Bath oil	2 in full bath
Body lotion	3 in 1 tbsp unscented body lotion
Massage blend	3 in 1 tbsp sweet almond oil

Avoid during pregnancy.

Spicy, Sultry and Very Hot

Clove

Profile

Vasco da Gama, the 15th century Portuguese navigator, is said to have discovered the clove tree growing in the Spice Islands of Indonesia. Once the most expensive spice, control of the clove trade was the source of sea wars for centuries between the Portuguese, the Dutch, the French and the English who all cultivated the tree in their far-flung territories.

The essential oil is distilled from the dried unopened buds of crimson flowers that are hand-picked or beaten from the clove tree at the end of the rainy season. The classic spicy scent, clove sizzles with a steamy sensuality as pervasive as a tropical heat. Strong and provocative, clove strengthens the system, builds vitality and courage, and arouses desire in a direct, frankly masculine manner. A sultry aphrodisiac, clove is commonly used in the East to help increase sexual energy and focus concentration on the subtle patterns of pure sensation.

● Stimulates energy ● Increases desire

Suggestions for Pleasure

Recommended only as a room fragrance, two drops of clove in an oil burner will transform an ordinary evening into a romantic encounter – hard to resist, impossible to forget.

Clove

Uses	Maximum Drops
Room fragrance	2 in oil burner

Avoid during pregnancy.

Inspiring

Frankincense

Profile

A holy oil given to Moses by the Lord and offered to the baby Jesus by the Magi, frankincense has been used for thousands of years in religious rituals to awaken and expand a sense of connection to the divine and the eternal. Also known as olibanum or oil of lebanon, frankincense is distilled from the hardened amber resin of a small gum tree that thrives in the desert habitat of civilization's holy lands. Beautiful, haunting, warm and musky with a faintly citrus overtone, the fragrance of frankincense improves with time, increasing in its power to evoke the timeless.

Like a high priestess of scent, ageless and serene, frankincense soothes and harmonizes the emotions. When fear and doubt overwhelm faith, when past sorrows dim present joys, when the mundane obstructs sight of the miraculous, the fragrance of frankincense helps induce a deeply tranquil state conducive to contemplation and prayer. A golden scent dedicated to the

- Relaxes mind and body

Goddess Aphrodite, and burnt by the sacred prostitutes of Greece to celebrate her gift of erotic love, frankincense is for couples who wish to steer the chariot of sexual desire to the sacred territory of love.

Frankincense

Uses	Maximum Drops
Room fragrance	4 in oil burner
Bath oil	6 in full bath
Body lotion	6 in 1 tbsp unscented body lotion
Massage blend	6 in 1 tbsp sweet almond oil

Suggestions for Pleasure

Just two drops of frankincense and one drop of rose combined in a handful of unperfumed body lotion inspire a wonderful feeling of relaxed well-being throughout the day. Or add to a warm bath and say a quiet word of thanks for birds that sing, for him, and everything.

Feminine and Full of Fun

Geranium

Profile

A fragrance for the fun of it, the scent of geranium is feminine and full of youthful gaiety. Fresh and floral with a slightly rosy tinge, geranium is one of the major oils of perfumery. Distilled from the highly aromatic *Pelargonium* species, geranium is said to have been a gift from Allah to the prophet Mohammed.

Radiating a sunny optimism that raises the spirits of even the most down-hearted lover, the fragrance of geranium is as enchanting as a good-natured, even-tempered girl. The scent is thus ideal to calm the emotions, while strengthening the inner confidence to enter (or re-enter) the social (or romantic) scene. Especially for those who express their fear through a rigid need for perfection and control, the lovely fragrance of geranium helps create an air of ease and contentment in which to enjoy the pleasures of a day.

● Elevates mood ● Builds confidence

Suggestions for Pleasure

A gorgeous scent, whether used as a room fragrance, bath oil or body lotion, geranium enhances a woman's enthusiasm for living.

Geranium

Uses	Maximum Drops
Room fragrance	3 in oil burner
Bath oil	3 in full bath
Body lotion	3 in 1 tbsp unscented body lotion
Massage blend	3 in 1 tbsp sweet almond oil

Irresistible

Jasmine

Profile

The fragrance of jasmine is undressed, erotic and utterly irresistible both to the woman who wears it, and the man who adores her. Known in its native India as "Queen of the Night," the fragrance distilled from jasmine's creamy star-shaped flowers is one of the "noble" oils of perfumery, along with rose and neroli. A scent that dissipates tension and increases a sense of self-worth, jasmine liberates the instinctual, intuitive forces from restraint and repression, and evokes feelings of well-being and love for life.

Like Kama, the Hindu god of love who pierces the heart of lovers with a jasmine-scented arrow, the fragrance from this night-blossoming flower casts a spell of pure desire. One of the great aphrodisiacs, revered for thousands of years in the East as an aid to lovemaking, jasmine helps liberate lovers caught in a web of fear, guilt, apathy or grief, and frees them to find fulfillment in love.

● Elevates mood ● Decreases inhibitions ● Increases desire

Suggestions for Pleasure

Like Cleopatra who soaked the sails of her barge in jasmine essential oil to seduce Mark Antony as they sailed down the Nile, this sexy scent wafted through a room causes any suitor to surrender his kingdom for love.

Jasmine	
Uses	**Maximum Drops**
Room fragrance	3 in oil burner
Bath oil	3 in full bath
Body lotion	3 in 1 tbsp unscented body lotion
Massage blend	3 in 1 tbsp sweet almond oil
Avoid during pregnancy.	

Elevating and Liberating

Juniper

Profile

A prehistoric plant species that was used in medieval Britain to drive out ghosts and keep witches at bay, the woody fresh scent distilled from the ripe berries of the juniper bush helps liberate a woman from those more modern demons: insecurity, inhibition, anger and fear.

A fragrance that builds strength on all levels, juniper lifts the emotions, enhances concentration, and increases energy. Especially for those who have been hurt by past relationships and now appear isolated and aloof, juniper helps restore the courage and the confidence to love again. During difficult periods, this fragrance from the hardy juniper bush, which once sheltered the Virgin Mary and her baby Jesus from King Herod's soldiers, offers couples a safe haven in which to find their way to harmony and happiness, again.

- Elevates mood • Builds confidence • Stimulates energy

Suggestions for Pleasure

On those days when self-confidence is sorely needed, but clearly lacking, a bath with the protective, purifying scent of juniper strengthens that inner voice, and helps a girl remember: she's got what it takes, so just smile.

Juniper

Uses	Maximum Drops
Room fragrance	4 in oil burner
Bath oil	4 in full bath
Body lotion	4 in 1 tbsp unscented body lotion
Massage blend	4 in 1 tbsp sweet almond oil

Avoid during pregnancy.

Soothing and Stabilizing

Lavender

Profile

A popular flower for thousands of years, lavender is native to the sunny mountainsides of the Mediterranean. Brought to the rest of Europe by the ancient Romans who planted it along their routes of conquest, lavender not only has superb healing properties, but also a fresh floral scent, which has made it a classic ingredient in many fine perfumes and cosmetics.

A particular favorite among English ladies of the Elizabethan and Stuart ages, lavender was traditionally sprinkled on the heads of young maidens to help preserve their chastity. Known for its ability to soothe and stabilize emotions, lavender essential oil is ideal for reducing stress and easing agitation. For those who feel the need for space and solitude before re-engaging with their mates, the scent of lavender helps promote a sense of calm contentment.

● Relaxes mind and body

Suggestions for Pleasure

The preferred bath oil of the Romans, several drops of lavender in a warm bath help a woman relax and luxuriate in a few undisturbed moments of healthy self-indulgence.

Lavender

Uses	Maximum Drops
Room fragrance	4 in oil burner
Bath oil	6 in full bath
Body lotion	6 in 1 tbsp unscented body lotion
Massage blend	6 in 1 tbsp sweet almond oil

Simply Delightful

Mandarin

Profile

Mandarin appeals to the senses with its orange-skinned roundness and deliciously moist fruit. Easy to peel, easy to enjoy, mandarin is one of life's sweet and simple pleasures. The full-bodied citrus scent obtained from the rind of the fruit is similarly delightful: cheerful, uplifting and uncomplicated.

The mandarin was a traditional present to the wise and powerful Mandarin rulers of the Chinese Empire for whom its succulence and bursting sensuality were presumably a grateful (and necessary) relief.

A fragrance ripe with optimism and a youthful belief in the goodness of life, mandarin essential oil helps lovers savor the gifts they offer – like juicy fruit – to one another.

• Elevates mood • Encourages spontaneity

Suggestions for Pleasure

On dark winter days, the scent of mandarin in a room brightens the mood and reminds lovers: soon it will be spring.

Mandarin

Uses	Maximum Drops
Room fragrance	5 in oil burner
Bath oil	3 in full bath
Body lotion	3 in 1 tbsp unscented body lotion
Massage blend	3 in 1 tbsp sweet almond oil

May cause photosensitivity;
avoid before exposure to the sun or ultraviolet light.

Romantic

Neroli

Profile

Neroli is an exquisite, elegant, even regal fragrance of femininity and grace. Composed and somewhat cool on the surface, yet intimating an unexpected volatility underneath, the beguiling scent extracted from the large white blossoms of the bitter orange tree is highly intriguing. A fragrance of seduction, without the passion of more earthy essential oils, neroli is both aloof in its perfection and imploring – the fair maiden of scent.

One of nature's most precious and most beautiful fragrances, the essence of orange blossoms allays anxiety and enhances communication and communion with another. A key ingredient in the love potion that enchanted the medieval lovers, Tristan and Isolde, the fairytale fragrance of neroli captivates the romantic heart with unspoken promises. Softly stirring sensual awareness, gently relieving shyness and inhibitions, neroli is an aphrodisiac to inspire and enrapture any knight.

- Relaxes mind and body • Increases desire

Suggestions for Pleasure

A traditional symbol of conjugal love, the scent of orange blossoms sprinkled on the marital bed helps couples find true happiness, forever after.

Neroli

Uses	Maximum Drops
Room fragrance	3 in oil burner
Bath oil	3 in full bath
Body lotion	3 in 1 tbsp unscented body lotion
Massage blend	3 in 1 tbsp sweet almond oil

Refreshing and Reviving

Orange

Profile

The fragrance of orange requires no analysis, it simply is: full of vitality, vivacious and refreshing. A traditional Chinese symbol of good luck and prosperity, orange has been used since the Middle Ages in love potions and fertility charms.

More a daytime than an evening scent, the citrus fragrance obtained from the brightly colored rind is uplifting and reviving. Particularly beneficial for demanding high-achievers, who have grown frustrated or apathetic from overwork, the fragrance of orange helps foster a more relaxed and optimistic approach to living. Cheerful and light-hearted, the scent of orange sweeps lovers up and renews their zest for giving.

- Elevates mood ● Encourages spontaneity

Suggestions for Pleasure

The scent of orange wafting through a dining room creates a sparkly, festive atmosphere – and stimulates the appetite.

Orange

Uses	Maximum Drops
Room fragrance	5 in oil burner
Bath oil	3 in full bath
Body lotion	3 in 1 tbsp unscented body lotion
Massage blend	3 in 1 tbsp sweet almond oil

May cause photosensitivity;
avoid before exposure to the sun or ultraviolet light.

Provocative and Passionate

Patchouli

Profile

Patchouli is a fragrance that cannot be ignored. Strong and earthy, musky and persistent, patchouli vibrates with a provocative physicality. Distilled from the dried leaves of a herbaceous shrub native to the tropics of the East, the grounding yet elevating scent of patchouli is said to be good for dreamers and was not surprisingly a favorite among the Flower Power children of the 1960s.

A passionate fragrance, patchouli frees the imagination, concentrates the mind and decreases inhibitions. Used as a liberating aphrodisiac for centuries, the sensuous scent of patchouli is for those who wish to use their bodies – unselfconsciously, confidently, courageously – like a splendid animal to express the anima or soul.

● Decreases inhibitions ● Increases desire

Suggestions for Pleasure

A few drops of patchouli in an essential oil burner heats up the room – just watch his temperature go up!

Patchouli

Uses	Maximum Drops
Room fragrance	2 in oil burner
Bath oil	2 in full bath
Body lotion	2 in 1 tbsp unscented body lotion
Massage blend	2 in 1 tbsp sweet almond oil

Invigorating

Pine

Profile

Distilled from the evergreen needles of a tree known to have survived the Ice Age, the crisp, woody fragrance of pine is energizing and invigorating. Imbued with the clean, sporty scent of the great outdoors, pine promotes expansive feelings of happiness and well-being, as well as the confidence to move forward with optimism.

The ancients believed the tall, upright and enduring pine was possessed by the spirit of Attis, god of fertility and eternal life, and considered the tree and its pine cones a symbol of male potency. Used as an aphrodisiac for centuries, pine excites a thoroughly male sexual reaction – and a similarly powerful female response.

● Stimulates energy ● Builds confidence ● Increases desire

Suggestions for Pleasure

A neck and shoulder massage with the stimulating scent of pine relieves mental fatigue, and gets him feeling frisky and full of fun.

Pine

Uses	Maximum Drops
Room fragrance	3 in oil burner
Bath oil	3 in full bath
Body lotion	3 in 1 tbsp unscented body lotion
Massage blend	3 in 1 tbsp sweet almond oil

Effortlessly Seductive

Rose

Profile

Rose is a flawless feminine scent of perfect beauty and harmony. A fragrance of poetry and myth, a symbol as much as a scent, rose is the Queen of Flowers and the perfume of angels.

Extracted from an ancient flower, which despite its delicacy has survived the poorest soil and the fiercest storms for more than 35 million years, the fragrance of rose is the embodiment of love in the feminine form. An exquisite scent, impossible to describe yet universally understood, rose enters and expands the heart – nurturing, calming and building the inner confidence to trust in the power of love.

The ultimate fragrance showered on Aphrodite as she emerged from the sea, rose heightens a sense of personal loveliness and pleasure, even pride, in the art of being a woman. Naturally feminine and effortlessly seductive, the

• Relaxes mind and body • Builds confidence • Increases desire

fragrance of rose is for all those who long for love – a love not only for the one, but also for the all. A love to share with generosity, a love to celebrate with roses.

Rose	
Uses	**Maximum Drops**
Room fragrance	3 in oil burner
Bath oil	3 in full bath
Body lotion	3 in 1 tbsp unscented body lotion
Massage blend	3 in 1 tbsp sweet almond oil

Suggestions for Pleasure

Like the Romans who scattered rose petals on the heads of newlyweds, the scent of rose in a room prepares a couple for the sensuous pleasures of long, leisurely Sundays in bed.

Strengthening and Stimulating

Rosemary

Profile

There is nothing erotic or sultry or even sensual about rosemary, and yet this essential oil is a great aphrodisiac. Strong and handsome, the scent resonates with a vitality that is self-assured and actively involved in living. One of Napoleon's favorite fragrances, rosemary is the exciting scent of power.

The penetrating herbal fragrance, distilled from the flowering tops of an evergreen shrub, is perhaps the most stimulating of all the essential oils. Physically, mentally and emotionally strengthening, rosemary has been used for millennia to increase the energy, concentration and confidence necessary for bold action. Yet the scent is open, friendly and very pleasing, making rosemary a key ingredient in many of the finest perfumes, including the classic eau de cologne.

Considered a gift from Aphrodite by the Greeks, the

● Stimulates energy ● Fortifies commitment

fragrance of rosemary exudes sexual energy. Not for the faint-hearted, the scent stirs a youthful lustiness, secure and confident and completely concentrated on its pleasure. A pleasure that is remembered like the love that engendered it, in times of conflict as well as contentment, rosemary strengthens the capacity not only to attract, but also to abide.

Rosemary

Uses	Maximum Drops
Room fragrance	4 in oil burner
Bath oil	3 in full bath
Body lotion	4 in 1 tbsp unscented body lotion
Massage blend	4 in 1 tbsp sweet almond oil

Avoid during pregnancy,
or if there is a history of epilepsy or hypertension.

Suggestions for Pleasure

In some older versions of the fairytale, Sleeping Beauty is roused after a hundred years not by the Prince's kiss, but by the scent of rosemary. Today, it is still an excellent essential oil to revive energy and enthusiasm,whether used in a bath, body lotion or room fragrancer. (But don't forget the kiss!)

Sensational

Sandalwood

Profile

According to the Koran, souls ascending to heaven were met by sensuous dark-eyed beauties who not only attended to their every whim, but created new desires which they soon satisfied. These women, the houris – or divine whores – where composed entirely of fragrance; they were pure pleasure, and their scent was sandalwood.

One of the oldest and most precious fragrances in the world, the rich woody scent with a sweet oriental undertone is distilled from the now endangered sandalwood tree, whose wood built the temples of the East. Used in India since at least the 5th century BC as a traditional aid to meditation – to the East what frankincense is to the West – sandalwood increases spiritual awareness and arouses sexual desire. Referred to in the famous Sanskrit love scriptures, the Kama Sutra, the scent of sandalwood is a renowned aphrodisiac to sharpen the senses, increase the imagination, build confidence, and

● Relaxes mind and body ● Excites imagination ● Increases desire

inspire that ultimate freedom – the freedom to surrender to an earthy sensuality and a heavenly bliss.

Sandalwood

Uses	Maximum Drops
Room fragrance	4 in oil burner
Bath oil	6 in full bath
Body lotion	6 in 1 tbsp unscented body lotion
Massage blend	6 in 1 tbsp sweet almond oil

Suggestions for Pleasure

A fragrance of enticement, the sensuous scent of sandalwood sprinkled in the bath stirs desire and prepares a woman for the pleasures of love.

Fascinating and Unforgettable

Vetivert

Profile

Difficult to fathom, yet totally fascinating, the fragrance of vetivert is like a stranger – unknown and irresistible. An earthy, musky scent that goes beneath the surface, vetivert is a fragrance to remember after even the briefest encounter; a fragrance to dream of, long after it's gone.

Obtained from the reddish roots of a wild tropical grass that thrives in the moist soil of the tropics, vetivert has been used for thousands of years in India as incense and perfume. Called the "oil of tranquillity" in the East and recommended in Sanskrit texts for anointing a bride, the scent of vetivert relieves tension and fear, inspires feelings of joyful submission, and provokes that most passionate desire: to penetrate and partake in the otherness of another.

• Relaxes mind and body • Increases desire

Suggestions for Pleasure

When used to perfume a room, the fragrance of vetivert dispels tension and encourages a carefree sensuality and free-spirited physicality.

Vetivert

Uses	Maximum Drops
Room fragrance	1 in oil burner
Bath oil	2 in full bath
Body lotion	2 in 1 tbsp unscented body lotion
Massage blend	2 in 1 tbsp sweet almond oil

Hypnotizing

Ylang Ylang

Profile

The fragrance of ylang ylang (pronounced ee-lang ee-lang) is distilled from the freshly picked, pendulous yellow flowers of the "perfume tree." Native to the tropics of Asia – Indonesia, Tahiti and the South Seas – the sweet floral scent has a hypnotizing effect, as powerful as any siren's song.

Like the land of its origins, ylang ylang is the lush, voluptuous scent of an island paradise. Separated from conventions, free of expectations, ylang ylang promotes a native physicality, at once innocent and erotic. One of nature's most reliable aphrodisiacs, ylang ylang helps create a relaxed, mellow mood, where fears and inhibitions are swept away on the soft breeze of its scent. Aroused and craving release, this seductive fragrance calls. To be shipwrecked on her shore, to experience the fullness of her love, to share the miracle of sunset, this is the temptation of ylang ylang for sailors, at home or at sea.

● Relaxes mind and body ● Decreases inhibitions ● Increases desire

Suggestions for Pleasure

A body lotion scented with the carefree, sexy fragrance of ylang ylang makes a girl want to kick off her shoes. Anyone for a walk on the beach?

Ylang Ylang

Uses	Maximum Drops
Room fragrance	3 in oil burner
Bath oil	3 in full bath
Body lotion	4 in 1 tbsp unscented body lotion
Massage blend	4 in 1 tbsp sweet almond oil

Fragrance Categories and Complementary Scents

Essential Oil	Fragrance Category	Blends Well With...
Bergamot	Citrus	Black Pepper, Chamomile, Frankincense, Geranium, Jasmine, Juniper, Lavender, Neroli, Orange, Patchouli, Rose, Rosemary, Sandalwood, Ylang Ylang
Black Pepper	Spicy	Citrus Oils, Cedarwood, Frankincense, Jasmine, Juniper, Rosemary, Sandalwood, Ylang Ylang
Cedarwood	Woodland	Citrus Oils, Black Pepper, Clary Sage, Frankincense, Jasmine, Juniper, Lavender, Neroli, Pine, Rose, Rosemary, Sandalwood
Chamomile	Herbal	Citrus Oils, Geranium, Lavender, Neroli, Rose, Sandalwood
Clary Sage	Herbal	Citrus Oils, Frankincense, Geranium, Jasmine, Juniper, Lavender, Rose, Rosemary, Sandalwood
Clove	Spicy	Citrus Oils
Frankincense	Musky	Black Pepper, Citrus Oils, Geranium, Jasmine, Lavender, Neroli, Rose, Sandalwood, Vetivert
Geranium	Floral	Citrus Oils, Frankincense, Jasmine, Juniper, Lavender, Neroli, Rose, Rosemary, Sandalwood
Jasmine	Floral	Black Pepper, Citrus Oils, Geranium, Lavender, Neroli, Rose, Sandalwood, Ylang Ylang

Fragrance Categories and Complementary Scents continued...

Essential Oil	Fragrance Category	Blends Well With...
Juniper	Woodland	Black Pepper, Citrus Oils, Clary Sage, Frankincense, Geranium, Lavender, Pine, Rosemary, Sandalwood
Lavender	Floral	Citrus Oils, Cedarwood, Chamomile, Frankincense, Geranium, Juniper, Neroli, Pine, Rose, Rosemary, Sandalwood, Ylang Ylang
Mandarin	Citrus	Bergamot, Black Pepper, Clary Sage, Clove, Frankincense, Geranium, Juniper, Neroli, Patchouli, Rosemary, Sandalwood, Vetivert, Ylang Ylang
Neroli	Floral	Cedarwood, Chamomile, Citrus Oils, Frankincense, Geranium, Jasmine, Lavender, Rose, Rosemary, Sandalwood, Vetivert
Orange	Citrus	Bergamot, Black Pepper, Clary Sage, Clove, Frankincense, Geranium, Juniper, Neroli, Patchouli, Rosemary, Sandalwood, Vetivert, Ylang Ylang
Patchouli	Musky	Bergamot, Frankincense, Geranium, Lavender, Neroli, Orange, Pine, Rose, Ylang Ylang
Pine	Woodland	Cedarwood, Lavender, Patchouli, Rosemary
Rose	Floral	Bergamot, Cedarwood, Chamomile, Clary Sage, Frankincense, Geranium, Jasmine, Lavender, Neroli, Patchouli, Sandalwood, Ylang Ylang

Essential Oil	Fragrance Category	Blends Well With...
Rosemary	Herbal	Black Pepper, Citrus Oils, Frankincense, Geranium, Juniper, Lavender, Neroli, Rose
Sandalwood	Woodland	Black Pepper, Cedarwood, Chamomile, Citrus Oils, Frankincense, Geranium, Jasmine, Juniper, Lavender, Neroli, Rose, Vetivert, Ylang Ylang
Vetivert	Musky	Frankincense, Geranium, Jasmine, Neroli, Orange, Rose, Sandalwood, Ylang Ylang
Ylang Ylang	Floral	Black Pepper, Citrus Oils, Frankincense, Jasmine, Lavender, Patchouli, Rose, Sandalwood

Bibliography

1. Ackerman, D.
A Natural History of Love. New York: Random House Inc., 1995.

2. Ackerman, D.
A Natural History of the Senses. New York: Random House Inc., 1990.

3. Allardice P.
Aphrodisiacs and Love Magic. New York: Avery Publishing Group Inc., 1989.

4. Anand M.
The Art of Sexual Magic. London: Judy Piatkus (Publishers) Ltd., 1995.

5. Arcier M.
Aromatherapy. London: Reed International Books Ltd., 1992.

6. Brown, D.
Aromatherapy. London: Headway Lifeguides (Hodder and Stoughton), 1993.

7. Chang J.
The Tao of Love. New York: Arkana (Penguin Books), 1977.

8. Chaplin J.
Love in an Age of Uncertainty. London: Aquarian (Harper Collins Publishers), 1993.

9. Cunningham, S.
Magical Aromatherapy - The Power of Scent.
St. Paul, Minnesota: Llewellyn Publications, 1989.

10. D'Aulaire I. and D'Aulaire E.
D'Aulaires' Book of Greek Myths. New York: Doubleday & Company, Inc., 1962.

11. Davis P.
Subtle Aromatherapy. London: The C.W. Daniel Company Ltd., 1991.

12. Fischer-Rizzi S.
Complete Aromatherapy Handbook, Essential Oils for Radiant Health. New York: Sterling Publishing Co. Inc., 1989.

13. Fromm E.
The Art of Loving. London: Thorsons (Harper Collins Publishers), 1995.

14. Genders R.
Perfume Through the Ages. New York: G.P. Putnam's Sons, 1972.

15. Guenther E.
The Essential Oils. London: Van Nostrand Co. (Reinhold), 1948.

16. Hamilton E.
Mythology. Timeless Tales of Gods and Goddesses. New York: Mentor Books, 1953.

17. Harding E.
The Way of All Women: Women's Mysteries. New York: Harper & Row, 1973.

18. Hirsch A.R. *Scentsational Sex. The Secret of Using Aroma for Arousal.* Boston: Element Books, Inc., 1998.

19. Houston J.
The Search for the Beloved: Journeys in Mythology and Sacred Psychology. Los Angeles: Jeremy Tarcher, 1987.

20. Husain S.
The Goddess. Power, Sexuality and the Feminine Divine. London: Duncan Baird Publishers, 2000.

21. Hutchinson J., McKenzie K. and Brass K.
The Perfumed Garden. London: Thorsons (Harper Collins Publishers), 1996. (Original text by Sheik Nefzawi; original translation (1885) by Sir Richard Burton).

22. Jackson J.
Aromatherapy. London: Dorling Kindersley Publishers Ltd., 1986.

23. Johnson R.A.
She. Understanding Female Psychology. New York: Harper & Row Publishers, 1976.

24. Johnson R.A.
The Psychology of Romantic Love. London: Arkana (Penguin Books), 1987.

25. Kitzinger S.
Woman's Experience of Sex. London: Dorling Kindersley, 1983.

26. Lacroix N.
The Art of Sensual Aromatherapy, A Lover's Guide to Using Aromatic Oils and Essences. London: Smith Gryphon Ltd., 1995.

27. Lavabre M.
Aromatherapy Workbook. Vermont: Healing Arts Press, Inner Traditions Inc., 1990.

28. Lawless J.
Aromatherapy and the Mind. London: Thorsons (Harper Collins Publishers), 1994.

29. Lawless J.
The Encyclopedia of Essential Oils. Dorset: Element Books Ltd., 1992.

30. Lee V.
Secrets of Venus. A Lover's Guide to Charms, Potions & Aphrodisiacs. Bluebell, Pa.: Mt. Ivy Press, 1996.

31. Lee W. and Lee L.
The Book of Practical Aromatherapy. San Fransisco: Keats Publishing Inc., 1992.

32. Le Guèrer A.
Scent: The Mysterious Power of Smell. New York: Chatto and Windus, 1993.

33. Lerner H.G.
The Dance of Intimacy. London: Harper Collins Publishers, 1990.

34. Mailhebiau P.
Portraits in Oils. London: The C.W. Daniel Company Ltd., 1996.

35. Mann A.T. and Lyle J.
Sacred Sexuality. Dorset: Element Books, 1995.

36. Maury M.
Marguerite Maury's Guide to Aromatherapy – The Secret of Life and Youth. London: The C.W. Daniel Company Ltd., 1989.

37. Miller R.A.
The Magical and Ritual Use of Aphrodisiacs. Vermont: Destiny Books, 1985.

38. Monaghan P.
The Book of Goddesses and Heroines. St. Paul, Minnesota: Llewellyn Publications, 1981.

39. Morris E.T.
Fragrance. The Story of Perfume from Cleopatra to Chanel. New York: Charles Scribner's Sons, 1984.

40. Peck M.S.
The Road Less Travelled. New York: Random Century, 1978.

41. Press B.
Herbs Green Guide. London:
New Holland (Publishers Ltd.),
1994.

42. Price S.
*Practical Aromatherapy – How
to Use Essential Oils to Restore
Vitality*. London: Thorsons
(Harper Collins Publishers),
1983.

43. Ritch B.A. and Ficke M.M.
*A History of Aphrodisiacs and
Related Subjects Yesterday and
Today*. California: Gems 'N'
Gold Publishing, 1984.

44. Ryman D.
*The Aromatherapy Handbook –
The Secret Healing Power of
Essential Oils*. London: The
C.W. Daniel Company Ltd.,
1989.

45. Stellar W.
The Directory of Essential Oils.
London: The C.W. Daniel
Company Ltd., 1992.

46. Stern M. and Bristow S.
The Courage to Love. London:
Judy Piatkus (Publishers) Ltd.,
1996.

47. Tisserand M.
Aromatherapy for Women.
Thorsons (Harper Collins
Publishers Ltd.), 1985.

48. Tisserand R.
The Art of Aromatherapy.
London: The C.W. Daniel
Company Ltd., 1977.

49. Valnet J.
The Practice of Aromatherapy.
London: The C.W. Daniel
Company Ltd., 1980.

50. Vroon P
Smell. The Secret Seducer.
New York: Farrar, Straus and
Giroux, 1994.

51. Warner M.
*From the Beast to the Blonde,
On Fairytales and their Tellers*.
London: Chatto & Windus,
1994.

52. Wildwood C.
*Aromatherapy. The Bloomsbury
Encyclopedia of Aromatherapy*.
London: Bloomsbury, 1996.

53. Wildwood C.
*Sensual Aromatherapy, Essential
Oils for Lovers*. London:
Headline Book Publishing, 1994.

54. Williamson M.
*A Return to Love, Reflections on
the Principles of A Course in
Miracles*. London: Aquarian
(Harper Collins Publishers),
1989.

55. Williamson M.
A Woman's Worth. London:
Random House, 1993.

56. Winter R.
*The Smell Book. Scents, Sex
and Society*. Philidelphia: J.B.
Lippincott Company, 1976.

57. Woolger J.B. and
Woolger R.J.
*The Goddess Within: A Guide
to the Eternal Myths that Shape
Women's Lives*. New York:
Fawcett, 1989.

58. Worwood V.A.
*Aromantics – Romance, Sex
and Nature's Essential Oils*.
Canada: Bantam Books, 1987.

59. Zeldin T.
*An Intimate History of
Humanity*. London: Minerva,
1994.

BIBLIOGRAPHY

Index

The Fragrant Veil
Essential Oil Recipes to Enhance
the Sensuous Pleasures of Living and Loving
ELISABETH MILLAR

SCENTS FOR THE SENSUOUS WOMAN

$\mathscr{E}$xplore the Sensual World of Scent

A sensuous woman's guide to the magical world of scent, *The Fragrant Veil, Essential Oils Recipes to Enhance the Sensuous Pleasures of Living and Loving*, presents a wide array of simple, beautiful recipes, using the pure fragrances of Nature's essential oils.

Aromatherapy without the therapy and purely for pleasure, this easy-to-use book describes the many ways essential oils may be enjoyed in the bath, in facial and body lotions, or as room fragrances.

Discover a wonderful way of using essential oils for pleasure, including…

- Aromatic baths to inspire tranquillity, increase vitality or stir sensuality…
- Fragrant oils to nourish, cleanse and tone the skin…
- Scented body lotions to soothe stress, lift the spirits, excite the imagination and inspire romance…
- Room fragrances to create a mood for love and laughter…

For more information and inspiration on using essential oils for love, romance and sensuous pleasure, please visit **www.fragrantveil.com**